SINATRA

Exclusive Distributors:
14/15 Berners Street, London W1T 3LJ
Music Sales Pty Limited
20 Resolution Drive, Caringbah, NSW 229, Australia.

This book © Copyright 1986 by Wise Publications.
ISBN 0.7119.0868.0
Order No. AM 62522

Designed by Pearce Marchbank Studio.
Compiled by Peter Lavender and Peter Evans.

Wise Publications.
London/NewYork/Sydney

SINATRA

All The Way.

Words: Sammy Cahn. Music: James Van Heusen.

That's how it's got to feel; Deep-er _____ than the deep blue sea is, that's how deep it goes, _ if it's real.

When some-bod - y needs you, it's no good un-less {he}{she} needs you ALL THE WAY. Through the good or lean years and for all the in be - tween years,

Angel Eyes.

Words: Earl Brent. Music: Matt Dennis.

Try to think_ that love's not a-round,_ Still it's un-com-fort-'bly near_

My old heart_ ain't gain-in' no ground_ be-cause my an-gel eyes ain't here._

Par-don me,___ but I "got-ta run"___

The fact's un-com-mon-ly clear,___ Got-ta find ___ who's

now "num-ber one"__ and why my an-gel eyes ain't here.___

'Scuse me while I dis-ap-pear.___

Because Of You.

Words and Music: Arthur Hammerstein and Dudley Wilkinson.

15

East Of The Sun
(And West Of The Moon).

Words and Music: Brooks Bowman.

live in a love-ly way, dear, Liv-ing on love and pale moon-light.

Just you and I,_____ for ev-er and a day,_____

Love will not die,_____ we'll

keep it that way,_____ Up a-mong the

Come Fly With Me.

Lyrics: Sammy Cahn. Music: Jimmy Van Heusen.

23

Fly Me To The Moon
(In Other Words).

Words and Music: Bart Howard.

How Insensitive.

Music: Antonio Carlos Jobim. Original Lyrics: Vinicius De Moraes.
English Lyrics: Norman Gimbel.

I'll Never Smile Again,
Until I Smile At You.

Words and Music: Ruth Lowe.

I'm Beginning To See The Light.

**Words and Music: Harry James, Duke Ellington,
Johnny Hodges and Don George.**

caused a spark,__ And my heart is on fire now,_____ I

nev-er made love by lan-tern shine,__ I nev-er saw rain-bows

half so fine,__ But now that your lips are burn-ing mine,__ I'm be-

gin-ning to see the light.__ I _____ I

I'm Gettin' Sentimental Over You.

Words: Ned Washington. Additional words: Reg Howard.
Music: Geo. Bassman.

I've Got You Under My Skin.

Words and Music: Cole Porter.

It's Nice To Go Trav'ling.

Words: Sammy Cahn. Music: James Van Heusen.

It Was A Very Good Year.

Words and Music: Ervin Drake.

The Lady Is A Tramp.

Words: Lorenz Hart. Music: Richard Rodgers.

Love And Marriage.

Words: Sammy Cahn. Music: James Van Heusen.

LOVE AND MAR - RIAGE,   LOVE AND   MAR - RIAGE,

Go to-geth - er like   a   horse and   car - riage, This   I tell   ya
It's an in - sti - tute you   can't dis - par - age, ask   the lo - cal

LOVE AND MAR-RIAGE, LOVE AND MAR-RIAGE, Go to-geth-er like a horse and car-riage, Dad was told by moth — er, You can't have one, You can't have none, You can't have one with-out the oth — er!

Oh Look At Me Now.

Words: John DeVries. Music: Joe Bushkin.

My Way.

Words: Paul Anka. Music: Claude François and Jacques Revaux.

Stormy Weather.

Words: Ted Koehler. Music: Harold Arlen.

Nancy (With The Laughing Face).

Words: Phil Silvers. Music: James Van Heusen.

NAN-CY with the laugh-ing face.___ She takes the NAN - CY with the laugh-ing face.___

Do you ev - er hear mis - sion bells ring -
What a won - der - ful treat ___ to come home___

___ ing? Well, she'll give you the ver - y same glow.___
___ to, When the long day has drawn ___ to a close.___

When she speaks you would think ___ it was sing -
There's the pat - ter of feet ___ to come home___

Something.

Words and Music: George Harrison.

Somethin' Stupid.

Words and Music: C. Carson Parks.

The Night We Called It A Day.

Words: Tom Adair. Music: Matt Dennis.

lov-ers' meet-ings, ro-man-tic greet-ings, To my mis-for-tune, I

found this a lie, For it was night when you

whis-pered "Good-bye," A night of mad-ness

that turned to sad-ness, much too soon: _____

Nice 'n' Easy.

Words: Marilyn Keith and Alan Bergman. Music: Lew Spence.

Old Devil Moon.

Words: E. Y. Harburg. Music: Burton Lane.

Strangers In The Night.

Music: Bert Kaempfert. Words: Charles Singleton and Eddie Snyder.

The Very Thought Of You.

Words and Music: Ray Noble.

near to you,_____ I see your face in ev' - ry

flow - er; Your eyes in stars a - bove,_____

poco rit.

a tempo

It's just the thought of you,__ The ver - y thought of you, my love._____

The ver - y love._____

poco rit.

L.H.

You Make Me Feel So Young.

Words: Mack Gordon. Music: Josef Myrow.

(Love Is) The Tender Trap.

Words: Sammy Cahn. Music: James Van Heusen.